A band came to play.

"My name is Stan," said a man.

"I want you to help us."

"I want you to clap," he said.

"Clap your hands and tap your feet."

"I want you to sing a song."

"Sing it with us."

The children sang with the band.

"Now clap as you sing," said Stan.

"Who wants to play in the band?"

The children put up their hands.

Everyone wanted to play.

"You can all play," said Stan.

Wilf hit the drum.

"Tap it," said Stan. "Don't bang it."

What a grand band!